PRIMARY MATHEMATICS 6B
WORKBOOK

SingaporeMath.com Inc

Marshall Cavendish
Education

Original edition published under the title Primary Mathematics Workbook 6B

© 1985 Curriculum Planning & Development Division

Ministry of Education, Singapore

Published by Times Media Private Limited

This American Edition

© 2003 Times Media Private Limited

© 2003 Marshall Cavendish International (Singapore) Private Limited

Published by Marshall Cavendish Education

An imprint of Marshall Cavendish International (Singapore) Private Limited

A member of Times Publishing Limited

Times Centre, 1 New Industrial Road, Singapore 536196

Customer Service Hotline: (65) 6411 0820

E-mail: fps@sg.marshallcavendish.com

Website: www.marshallcavendish.com/education/sg

Distributed by

SingaporeMath.com Inc

404 Beavercreek Road #225

Oregon City, OR 97045

U.S.A.

Website: http://www.singaporemath.com

First published 2003

Second impression 2003

Reprinted 2005 (twice), 2006, 2007, 2008

ISBN 978-981-01-8517-6

Printed in Singapore by C.O.S. Printers Pte Ltd

ACKNOWLEDGEMENTS

Our special thanks to Richard Askey, Professor of Mathematics (University of Wisconsin, Madison), Yoram Sagher, Professor of Mathematics (University of Illinois, Chicago), and Madge Goldman, President (Gabriella and Paul Rosenbaum Foundation), for their indispensable advice and suggestions in the production of Primary Mathematics (U.S. Edition).

CONTENTS

EXERCISE 1

1.　Divide. Then use the pictures to check your answers.

(a)   ⇨

$$3 \div \frac{1}{4} = 3 \times 4$$
$$=$$

3 wholes can be divided into _____ quarters.

(b)   ⇨

$$2 \div \frac{1}{5} = 2 \times$$
$$=$$

2 wholes can be divided into _____ fifths.

(c)  ⇨

$$4 \div \frac{1}{2} = 4 \times$$
$$=$$

4 wholes can be divided into _____ halves.

(d)  ⇨

$$3 \div \frac{1}{6} = 3 \times$$
$$=$$

3 wholes can be divided into _____ sixths.

2. Divide.

(a) $3 \div \frac{1}{2} = 3 \times 2$ $=$	(b) $3 \div \frac{1}{5} = 3 \times$ $=$
(c) $4 \div \frac{1}{3} =$	(d) $4 \div \frac{1}{4} =$
(e) $5 \div \frac{1}{5} =$	(f) $6 \div \frac{1}{3} =$
(g) $1 \div \frac{1}{8} =$	(h) $7 \div \frac{1}{6} =$

EXERCISE 2

1. Divide.

(a) $\dfrac{1}{3} \div 3 = \dfrac{1}{3} \times \dfrac{1}{3}$ $= $	(b) $\dfrac{1}{2} \div 6 = \dfrac{1}{2} \times$ $=$
(c) $\dfrac{1}{6} \div 4 =$	(d) $\dfrac{4}{5} \div 2 =$
(e) $\dfrac{2}{5} \div 4 =$	(f) $\dfrac{8}{9} \div 4 =$
(g) $\dfrac{3}{4} \div 2 =$	(h) $\dfrac{2}{3} \div 6 =$

EXERCISE 3

1. Divide.

(a) $\frac{1}{2} \div \frac{1}{3} =$

(b) $\frac{1}{3} \div \frac{1}{6} =$

(c) $\frac{4}{5} \div \frac{1}{5} =$

(d) $\frac{5}{8} \div \frac{1}{4} =$

(e) $4 \div \frac{4}{5} =$

(f) $6 \div \frac{3}{4} =$

(g) $\frac{1}{8} \div \frac{3}{4} =$

(h) $\frac{4}{9} \div \frac{2}{3} =$

EXERCISE 4

1. Find the value of each of the following:

(a) $\dfrac{3}{4} - \dfrac{3}{8} + \dfrac{1}{2}$

=

(b) $\dfrac{3}{8} + \dfrac{2}{3} - \dfrac{1}{4}$

=

(c) $\dfrac{2}{3} \times \dfrac{3}{8} \times 2$

=

(d) $\dfrac{4}{9} \div 2 \div \dfrac{1}{6}$

=

(e) $7 \div 2 \times \dfrac{2}{7}$

=

(f) $\dfrac{5}{6} \times \dfrac{4}{5} \div 4$

=

(g) $\dfrac{3}{5} \times \dfrac{2}{9} \div \dfrac{3}{10}$

=

(h) $\dfrac{3}{8} \div \dfrac{3}{4} \times \dfrac{2}{5}$

=

EXERCISE 5

1.   Find the value of each of the following:

(a) $\dfrac{4}{5} \times \dfrac{5}{6} - \dfrac{2}{3}$
 	
    $=$
	(b) $\dfrac{3}{4} \div \dfrac{9}{10} - \dfrac{1}{2}$
	
	    $=$

(c) $3 + 4 \times \dfrac{5}{8}$
 	
    $=$
	(d) $5 - \dfrac{2}{3} \div \dfrac{1}{6}$
	
	    $=$

(e) $\dfrac{5}{6} - \dfrac{2}{3} \times \dfrac{3}{8}$
 	
    $=$
	(f) $\dfrac{3}{4} + \dfrac{2}{5} \div \dfrac{3}{10}$
	
	    $=$

(g) $\dfrac{1}{2} + 3 \times \dfrac{1}{4} \div \dfrac{3}{8}$
 	
    $=$
	(h) $\dfrac{1}{2} + \dfrac{5}{6} \times \dfrac{9}{10} - \dfrac{1}{3}$
	
	    $=$

2. Find the value of each of the following:

(a) $\dfrac{7}{8} - \dfrac{3}{4} + \dfrac{1}{2}$ =	(b) $\dfrac{1}{3} + \dfrac{5}{6} - \dfrac{1}{2}$ =	(c) $\dfrac{2}{3} \times \dfrac{1}{8} \div \dfrac{1}{2}$ =
(d) $\dfrac{4}{5} - \dfrac{3}{5} \times \dfrac{1}{6}$ =	(e) $\dfrac{1}{2} + 8 \div \dfrac{4}{9}$ =	(f) $\dfrac{4}{5} \div \dfrac{3}{5} \times \dfrac{1}{3}$ =

Shade the spaces which contain the answers. This will help Annie find her pen.

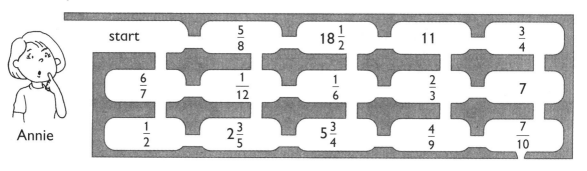

EXERCISE 6

1. Find the value of each of the following:

(a) $(\frac{3}{5} - \frac{1}{3}) \times \frac{5}{8}$ =	(b) $\frac{3}{4} \div (\frac{1}{6} + \frac{2}{3})$ =
(c) $\frac{2}{5} + (5 - 3) \div \frac{4}{5}$ =	(d) $\frac{4}{5} - (1 - \frac{2}{5}) \div 3$ =
(e) $\frac{6}{7} \times (\frac{1}{4} + \frac{1}{3}) - \frac{1}{3}$ =	(f) $\frac{3}{4} + (\frac{1}{4} + \frac{3}{8}) \div \frac{5}{6}$ =
(g) $(1 - \frac{3}{8}) \div (\frac{1}{3} \times \frac{1}{2})$ =	(h) $4 \div (\frac{1}{5} + \frac{1}{4}) \times \frac{3}{10}$ =

2. Find the value of each of the following:

(a) $\frac{1}{2} + \frac{1}{2} \times \frac{1}{4} - \frac{3}{8}$

=

O

(b) $\frac{2}{5} \times (5 - 3) \div \frac{7}{10}$

=

I

(c) $\frac{2}{3} \div 4 \times \frac{3}{4}$

=

C

(d) $2 \div (\frac{1}{2} + \frac{1}{4}) \times \frac{3}{8}$

=

E

(e) $(1 - \frac{3}{8}) \div (\frac{1}{2} + \frac{1}{3})$

=

S

(f) $\frac{1}{6} + \frac{5}{6} \div \frac{5}{6} - \frac{2}{3}$

=

L

What kind of triangle has two equal sides?
Write the letters which match the answers to find out.

$1\frac{1}{7}$	$\frac{3}{4}$	$\frac{1}{4}$	$\frac{3}{4}$	$\frac{1}{8}$	1	$\frac{1}{2}$	1	$\frac{3}{4}$

EXERCISE 7

1. A shopkeeper had 150 lb of rice. He sold $\frac{2}{5}$ of it and packed the remainder equally into 5 bags. Find the weight of the rice in each bag.

---

2. Peter had 400 stamps. $\frac{5}{8}$ of them are U.S. stamps and the rest are Canadian stamps. He gave $\frac{1}{5}$ of the U.S. stamps to his friend. How many stamps did he have left?

3. Kyle gave $\frac{2}{7}$ of his money to his wife and spent $\frac{3}{5}$ of the remainder. If he had $300 left, how much money did he have at frst?

---

4. $\frac{2}{3}$ of the beads in a box are red, $\frac{1}{4}$ are yellow and the rest are blue. There are 42 more red beads than blue beads. How many beads are there altogether?

EXERCISE 8

1. Lucy spent $\frac{3}{5}$ of her money on a handbag. She spent the rest of the money on a dress and a belt. The handbag cost twice as much as the dress. The dress cost $20 more than the belt. How much money did she have at first?

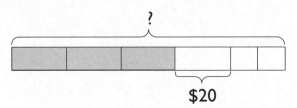

16

2. Gary spent $48 on a watch. He spent $\frac{1}{3}$ of the remainder on a pen. If he still had $\frac{1}{2}$ of his money left, how much money did he have at first?

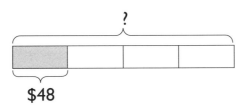

EXERCISE 9

1. Draw a circle with the given line as a radius.

2. Draw a circle with the given line as a diameter.

3.   Draw a circle of radius 5 cm.

4.   Draw a circle of diameter 8 cm.

5.   Measure the radius and diameter of each circle.
     (a)

Radius =

Diameter =

(b)

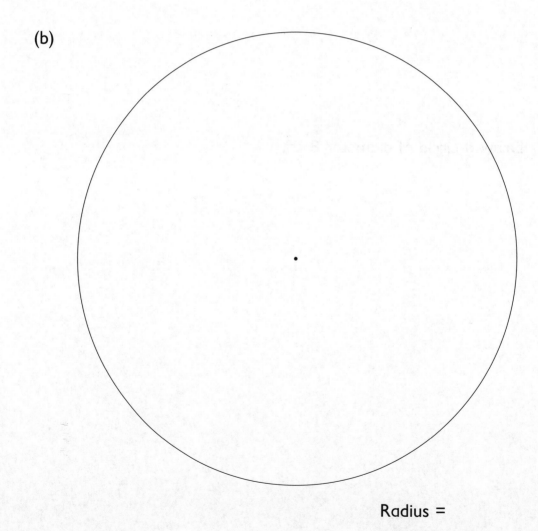

Radius =

Diameter =

EXERCISE 10

1. Match each circle with its circumference.

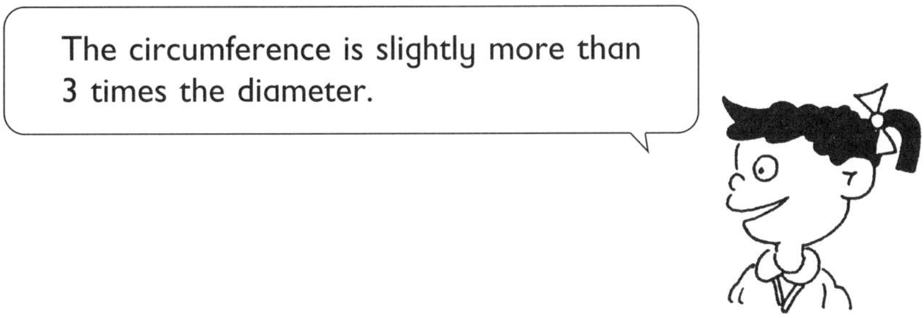

The circumference is slightly more than 3 times the diameter.

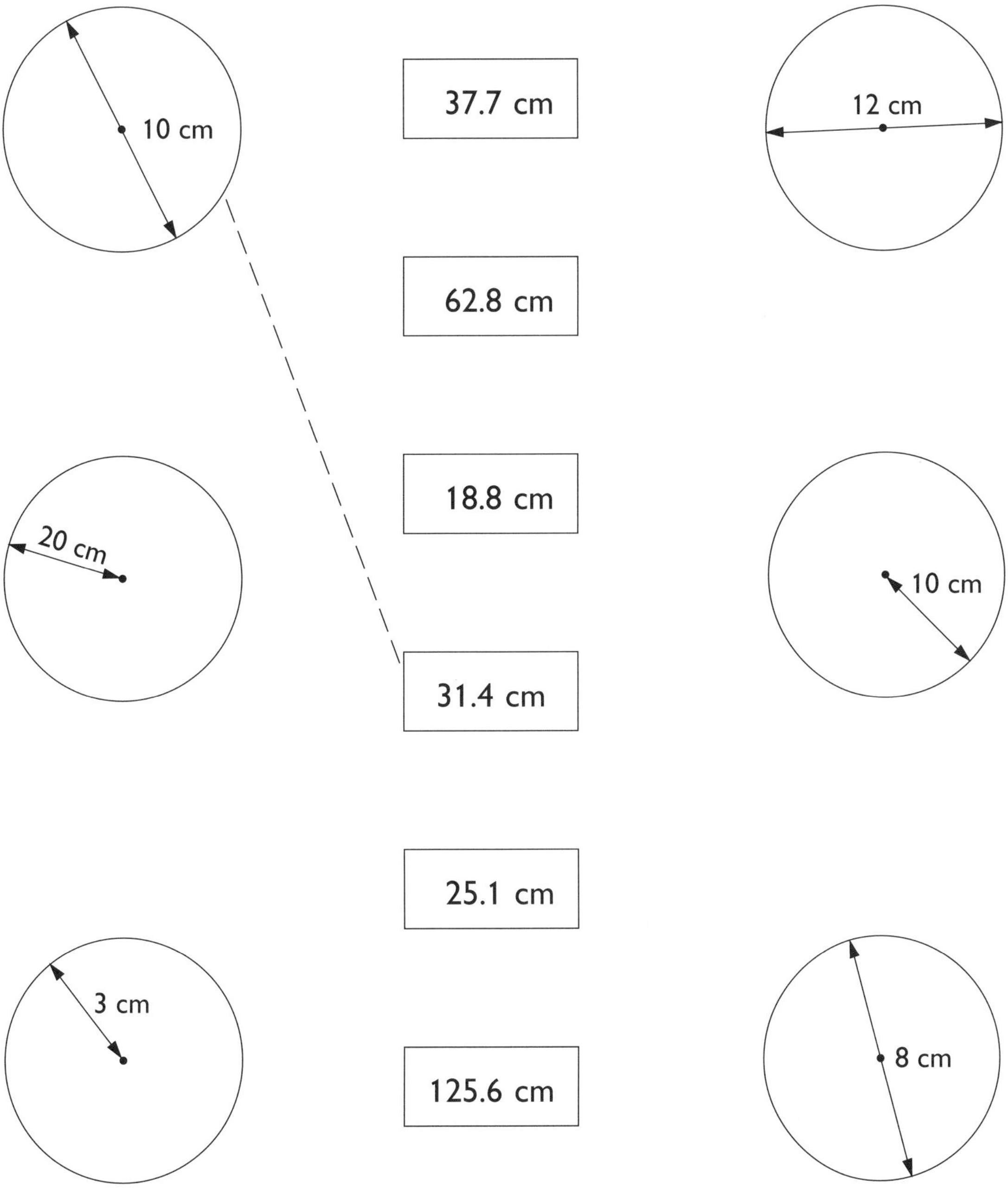

10 cm

20 cm

3 cm

37.7 cm

62.8 cm

18.8 cm

31.4 cm

25.1 cm

125.6 cm

12 cm

10 cm

8 cm

2. Find the circumference of each circle.

(a)

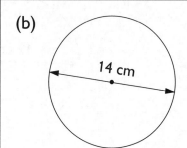

5 cm

(Take π = 3.14)

(b)

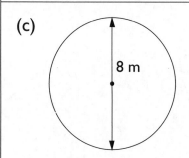

14 cm

$\left(\text{Take } \pi = \dfrac{22}{7}\right)$

(c)

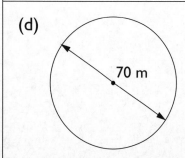

8 m

(Take π = 3.14)

(d)

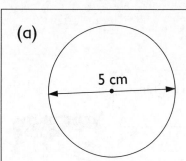

70 m

$\left(\text{Take } \pi = \dfrac{22}{7}\right)$

3. Find the circumference of each circle.

(a)

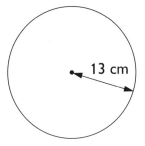

(Take π = 3.14)

(b)

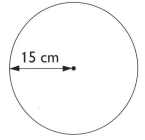

(Take π = 3.14)

(c)

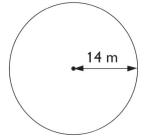

$\left(\text{Take } \pi = \dfrac{22}{7} \right)$

(d)

$\left(\text{Take } \pi = \dfrac{22}{7} \right)$

EXERCISE 11

1. Find the perimeter of each semicircular shape.

    (a)

    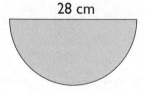

    28 cm

    $\left(\text{Take } \pi = \dfrac{22}{7}\right)$

    (b)

    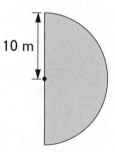

    10 m

    (Take π = 3.14)

2. The figure shows a piece of paper which has a shape of a quarter circle. Find its perimeter. (Take π = 3.14)

    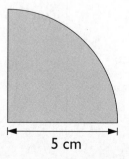

    5 cm

3. The figure shows a circle within a square. Find the circumference of the circle. (Take π = 3.14)

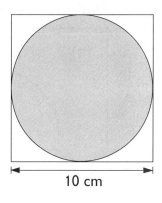

10 cm

4. The curve is made up of 2 semicircles as shown. Find its length. Leave your answer in terms of π.

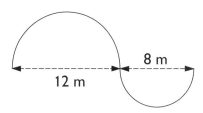

8 m

12 m

EXERCISE 12

1. Find the area of each of the following circles. (Take π = 3.14)

(a)

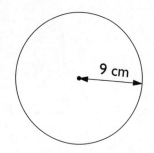

9 cm

(b)

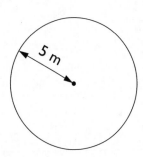

5 m

(c)

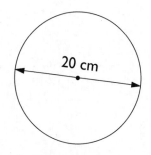

20 cm

(d)

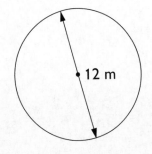

12 m

2. Find the area of each of the following circles. $\left(\text{Take } \pi = \dfrac{22}{7}\right)$

(a)

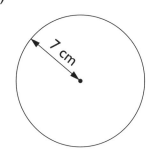

(b)

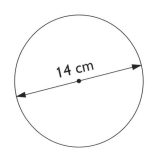

(c)

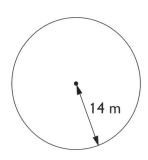

(d)

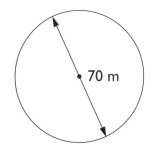

EXERCISE 13

1.   The figure shows a circle within a square. Find the area of the circle. (Take π = 3.14)

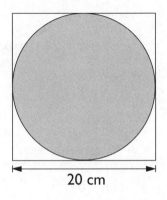

20 cm

2.   The figure shows a cardboard which has a shape of a quarter circle. Find its area. (Take π = 3.14)

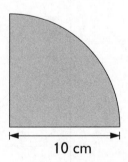

10 cm

3. Find the area of each semicircular shape.

$$\left(\text{Take } \pi = \frac{22}{7}\right)$$

(a)

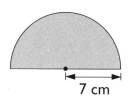

7 cm

(b)

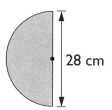

28 cm

EXERCISE 14

1. The following figures are made up of semicircles and quarter circles.

    Find the area of each figure. $\left(\text{Take } \pi = \dfrac{22}{7}\right)$

    (a)

    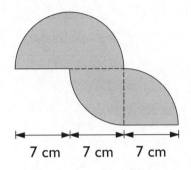

    7 cm   7 cm   7 cm

    (b)

    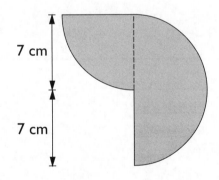

    7 cm

    7 cm

    (c)

    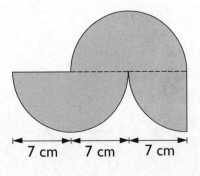

    7 cm   7 cm   7 cm

2. The following figures are made up of semicircles and quarter circles. Find the area of each figure in terms of π.

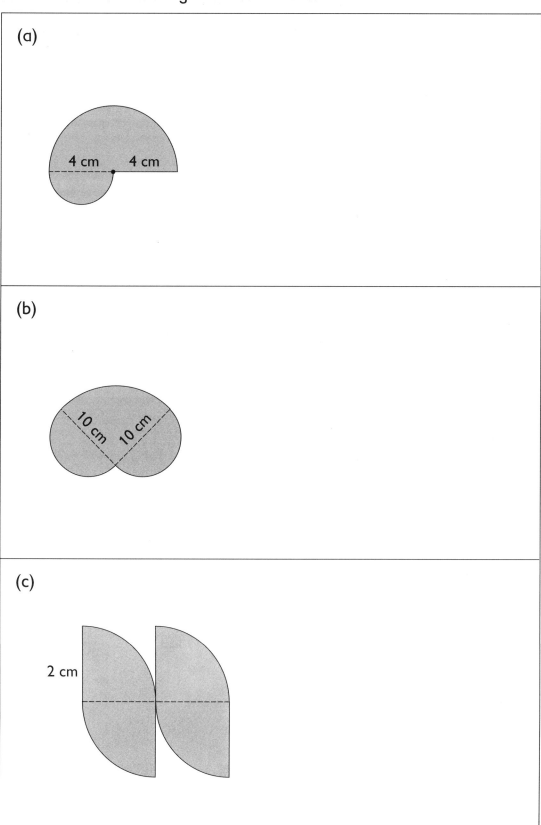

(a)

4 cm   4 cm

(b)

10 cm   10 cm

(c)

2 cm

3.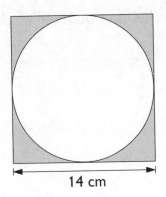

14 cm

The figure shows a square and a circle. Find the total area of the shaded parts. $\left(\text{Take } \pi = \frac{22}{7}\right)$

4.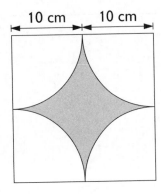

10 cm   10 cm

The figure shows a square and 4 quarter circles. Find the area of the shaded part. (Take $\pi = 3.14$)

5.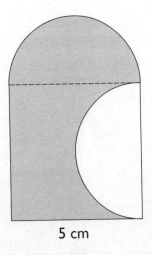

5 cm

The figure shows a square and 2 semicircles. Find the total area of the shaded parts.

EXERCISE 15

Write the answers in the boxes.

1. The figure is made up of a square and a semicircle. $\left(\text{Take } \pi = \dfrac{22}{7}\right)$

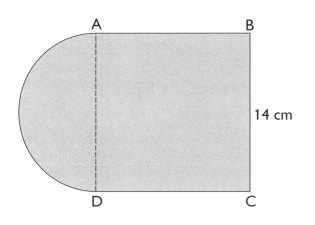

(a) Area of the semicircle

= [ ]

(b) Area of square ABCD

= [ ]

(c) Area of the figure

= [ ]

2. The figure is made up of a rectangle and two semicircles. (Take π = 3.14)

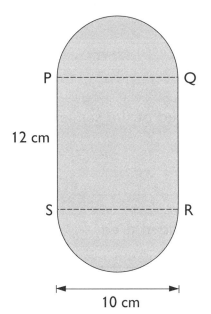

(a) Area of the two semicircles

= [ ]

(b) Area of rectangle PQRS

= [ ]

(c) Area of the figure

= [ ]

3. The figure is made up of a triangle and a semicircle. (Take π = 3.14)

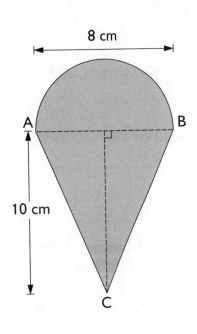

8 cm

A   B

10 cm

C

(a) Area of the semicircle

=

(b) Area of triangle ABC

=

(c) Area of the figure

=

4. The figure shows a rectangle and a semicircle.

$$\left(\text{Take } \pi = \frac{22}{7} \right)$$

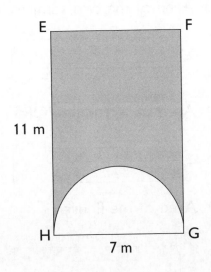

E   F

11 m

H   G

7 m

(a) Area of rectangle EFGH

=

(b) Area of the semicircle

=

(c) Shaded area

=

5.   The figure shows a square and two semicircles.
     (Take π = 3.14)

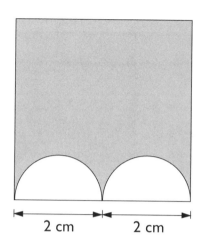

2 cm   2 cm

(a) Area of the square

= _____

(b) Area of the two semicircles

= _____

(c) Shaded area

= _____

6.   The figure shows a rectangle and two semicircles.
     (Take π = 3.14)

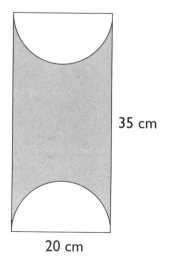

35 cm

20 cm

(a) Area of the rectangle

= _____

(b) Area of the two semicircles

= _____

(c) Shaded area

= _____

EXERCISE 16

1. The figure shows a rectangle and a semicircle. Find the perimeter of the shaded part. (Take π = 3.14)

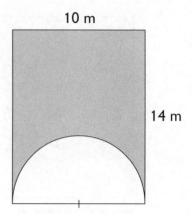

10 m

14 m

2. The figure is made up of a square, a semicircle and a triangle. Find its area. (Take π = 3.14)

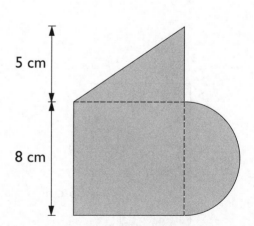

5 cm

8 cm

3. The figure is made up of a square and 3 semicircles. Find its area and perimeter. (Take π = 3.14)

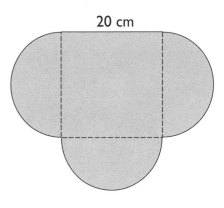

20 cm

4. The figure shows a square, a semicircle and a quarter circle. Find the area and perimeter of the shaded part. (Take π = 3.14)

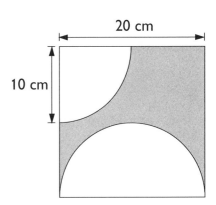

20 cm

10 cm

EXERCISE 17

1. The pie chart shows how a group of students travel to school.

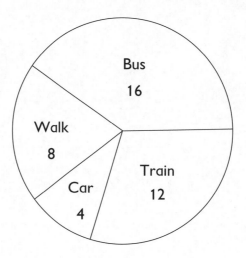

(a) How many students go to school by bus?

(b) How many students go to school by train?

(c) How many students are there altogether?

(d) What fraction of the students walk to school?

(e) What fraction of the students go to school by car?

2. The pie chart shows the different types of vehicles involved in road accidents in a city last year.

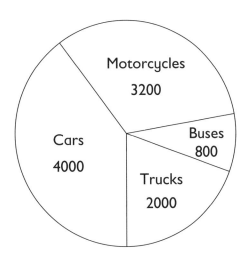

(a) Which type of vehicles had the highest number of road accidents last year?

(b) How many trucks were involved in road accidents?

(c) What was the total number of vehicles involved in road accidents?

(d) What fraction of the vehicles involved in road accidents were buses?

(e) What fraction of the vehicles involved in road accidents were motorcycles?

3. Betty made four types of sandwiches for a party. The pie chart represents the number of each type of sandwiches.

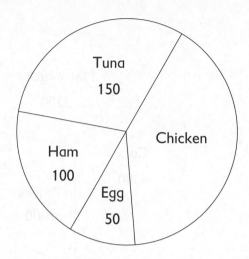

(a) How many tuna sandwiches and ham sandwiches did Betty make?

(b) How many chicken sandwiches did Betty make?

(c) How many sandwiches did she make altogether?

(d) What percentage of the sandwiches were ham sandwiches?

(e) How many times as many tuna sandwiches as egg sandwiches were there?

4. The pie chart shows what Henry does with his weekly allowance.

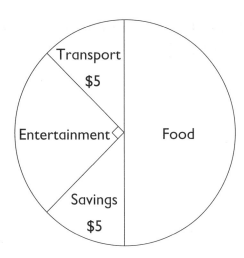

(a) What fraction of his allowance does he save?

(b) How much is his weekly allowance?

(c) What fraction of his allowance does he spend on food?

(d) What percentage of his allowance does he spend on entertainment?

(e) Find the ratio of the amount spent on transport to the amount spent on food.

EXERCISE 18

1. There are 200 vehicles in a parking lot. The pie chart represents the number of each type of vehicles.

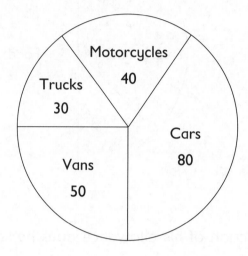

Express the number of each type of vehicles as a fraction of the total number of vehicles and write it on the pie chart below.

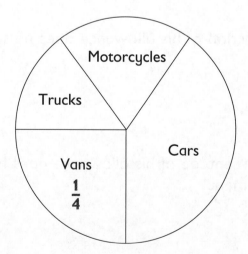

2. A group of 400 adults were asked how often they jog in a week. The pie chart shows the results.

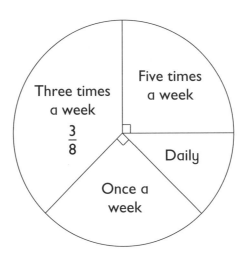

(a) What fraction of the adults jog three times a week?

(b) What fraction of the adults jog once a week?

(c) What fraction of the adults jog daily?

(d) How many adults jog three times a week?

(e) How many adults jog five times a week?

3. A group of 180 students were asked to choose the club they would like to join. The pie chart represents their choices.

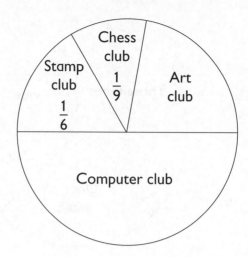

(a) What fraction of the students chose the computer club?

(b) What fraction of the students chose the art club?

(c) How many students chose the chess club?

(d) How many students chose the stamp club?

(e) How many more students chose the stamp club than the chess club?

4. A group of children were asked to choose their favorite ice cream flavor from chocolate, peach, vanilla and strawberry. The pie chart represents their choices.

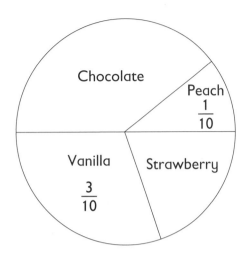

(a) Which was the most popular ice cream flavor?

(b) What fraction of the children liked chocolate ice cream?

(c) What percentage of the children liked vanilla ice cream?

(d) What percentage of the children liked strawberry ice cream?

(e) If 48 children liked vanilla ice cream, how many children were there in the group?

EXERCISE 19

1. The pie chart shows how Nicole spent $1000 on four electrical items.

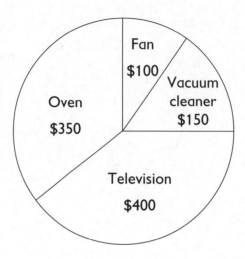

Find the percentage of money spent on each item and write it on the pie chart below.

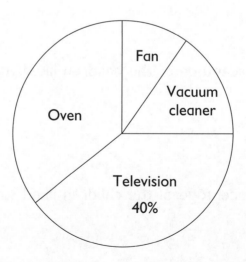

2. A sports shop sold 80 balls on a certain day. The pie chart represents the quantity of each type of balls sold.

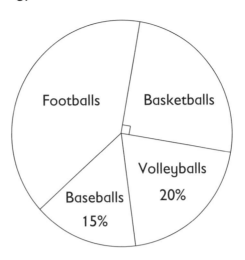

(a) What percentage of the balls sold were baseballs?

(b) What percentage of the balls sold were basketballs?

(c) What percentage of the balls sold were footballs?

(d) How many baseballs were sold?

(e) How many volleyballs were sold?

3. Lukas sold 40 kg of vegetables. The pie chart represents the amount of each type of vegetables sold.

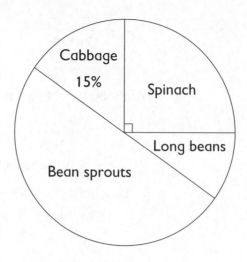

(a) How many types of vegetables did Lukas sell?

(b) What percentage of the weight of vegetables sold were long beans?

(c) How many kilograms of cabbage did he sell?

(d) How many kilograms of bean sprouts did he sell?

(e) How many kilograms of spinach did he sell?

4. A basket contains mangoes, oranges, pears and apples. The pie chart represents the number of each of these fruits in the basket.

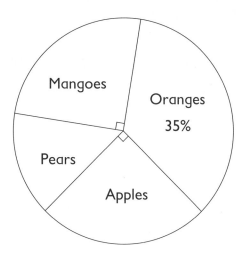

(a) What fraction of the total number of fruits are oranges?

(b) What percentage of the total number of fruits are apples?

(c) What percentage of the total number of fruits are pears?

(d) Find the total number of fruits if there are 30 mangoes.

(e) Find the number of oranges if there are 30 mangoes.

REVIEW 1

Write the answers in the boxes.

1. In **670,842**, the value of the digit **7** is $7 \times$ ■.
   What is the missing number in the ■?

2. A library has 247,495 books. Round off the number of books to the nearest thousand.

3. What is the number indicated by the arrow?

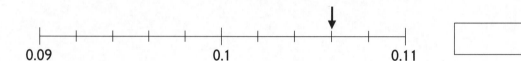

4. Find the value of $6.3 - 3.45$

5. What is the missing number in each ■?

   (a) $\dfrac{13}{5} = 2 + \dfrac{■}{5}$

   (b) $4\dfrac{1}{2} = ■ \times \dfrac{1}{2}$

6. Express 25 cents as a fraction of $2 in its simplest form.

7. Express 750 g as a percentage of 2 kg.

8. Find the value of each of the following:

   (a) $\dfrac{2}{3} \div \dfrac{5}{6}$

   (b) $\dfrac{5}{8} \times (\dfrac{3}{4} + \dfrac{2}{5})$

9. The average height of 4 boys is 1.65 m. One boy is 1.68 m tall. Find the average height of the other 3 boys.

10. Ian, John and Juan shared a sum of money in the ratio 4 : 7 : 9. What percentage of the sum of money did John receive?

11. The usual price of a refrigerator is $800. It is sold at a discount of 15%. Find the selling price.

12. A boy is cycling at a speed of 200 m/min. How long will he take to cycle a distance of 4 km?

13. The number of boys is $\frac{7}{10}$ of the total number of students in a class. If there are 16 more boys than girls in the class, how many students are there altogether?

14. At a train station, the ratio of the number of children to the number of adults is 4 : 7. There are 132 people altogether. How many more adults than children are there?

15. 450 children take part in an art competition. If there are 25% more boys than girls, how many more boys than girls are there?

16. The table shows the rates of charges for parking at a parking lot.

8:00 a.m. to 5:00 p.m.	$1.50 per hour
After 5:00 p.m.	$1.00 per hour

Mr. Ray parked his car from 3:00 p.m. to 6:10 p.m. How much parking fee did he pay?

17. Find the area of the figure. (All the angles are right angles.)

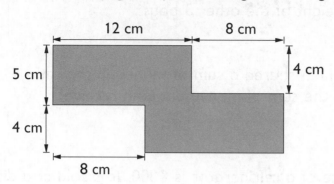

18. The figure is made up of a rectangle and two equilateral triangles. Find its perimeter.

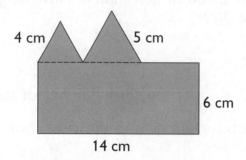

19. The figure is made up of a semicircle, a rectangle and a triangle. Find its area. (Take $\pi = 3.14$)

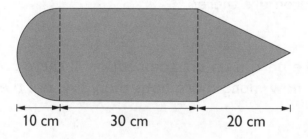

20. The figure is made up of 4 semicircles. Find its perimeter in terms of π.

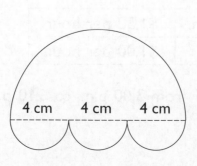

21. The figure shows half of a symmetric figure which has the dotted line as a line of symmetry. Complete the symmetric figure.

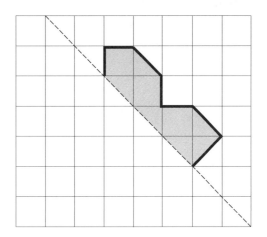

22. The bar graph shows the weights of 5 boys.

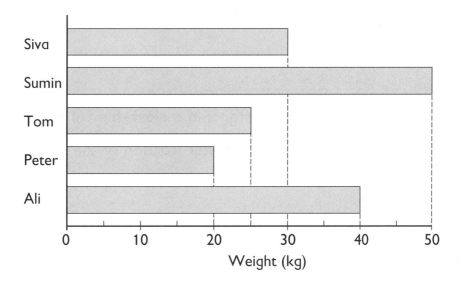

(a) Find the difference in weight between Sumin and Peter.

(b) What is the ratio of Ali's weight to Tom's weight?

(c) Express Siva's weight as a fraction of Sumin's weight.

23.   Wendy sold 200 tarts at $0.40 each. With the money she received from the sale of tarts, she bought 8 plates and had $28.80 left. Find the cost of 1 plate.

---

24.   There are as many boys as girls in a class. If $\frac{2}{5}$ of the boys and $\frac{1}{2}$ of the girls go to school by bus, what fraction of the students in the class go to school by bus?

25. Three boys, Ali, Ben and Rajah share a sum of money. Ali's share is $60. The ratio of Ben's share to Rajah's share is 1 : 3. If Ali's share is $15 more than Ben's share, how much money is Rajah's share?

---

26. There were as many boys as girls in a computer club last year. This year, 11 boys joined the club and the membership increased by 10%. How many boys were in the club last year?

REVIEW 2

Write the answers in the boxes.

1. In 20.45, which digit is in the hundredths place?

2. What is the missing number in each ■?

   (a) $6.805 = 6 + \dfrac{8}{■} + \dfrac{5}{1000}$

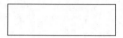

   (b) $6 \times \dfrac{4}{5} = \dfrac{4}{5} + \dfrac{4}{5} + ■ \times \dfrac{4}{5}$

3. Find the value of

   (a) $27 + 96 \div 12 \div 4$

   (b) $(45 + 27) \div (17 - 8)$

4. Which one of the following is the best estimate of the value of 456×0.29?

   50,   150,   500,   1500

5. What fraction of the figure is shaded?

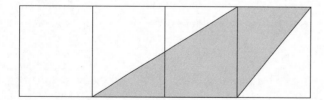

6. Write $\dfrac{24}{42}$ in its simplest form.

7. Write $3\dfrac{5}{7}$ as a decimal correct to 2 decimal places.

8. Find the missing number in the ■.

   $32 : 16 : 48 = 2 : 1 : ■$

9. The total cost of 3 T-shirts and a pair of shorts is $54. Each T-shirt costs $5 more than the pair of shorts. Find the cost of the pair of shorts.

10. Brian bought 54 mangoes. He gave away $\frac{2}{3}$ of the mangoes and ate $\frac{1}{6}$ of the remainder. How many mangoes did he have left?

11. A container was $\frac{1}{2}$ filled with water. When 200 ml of water was poured out, it became $\frac{1}{3}$ full. Find the capacity of the container.

12. The ratio of the number of Austin's stamps to the number of Henry's stamps is 5 : 3. They have 1000 stamps altogether. How many stamps must Austin give Henry so that they will each have an equal number of stamps?

13. The price of a computer was increased by 10% to $2420. What was the price before the increase?

14. Mary's savings is 25% more than Susan's savings. If Mary has $200 more than Susan, find their total savings.

15. Jacob walked from his house to a supermarket which was 0.8 km away. His average speed was 50 m/min. Find the time taken in minutes.

16. Find the value of the following expressions when $a = 3$.
    (a) $\frac{2a - 3}{4}$

    (b) $40 - a^3$

17. The average weight of 3 girls is x kg. When another girl joins the group, the average weight of the 4 girls is 30 kg. Find the weight of the 4th girl in terms of x.

18. Find the area of the figure. (All the angles are right angles.)

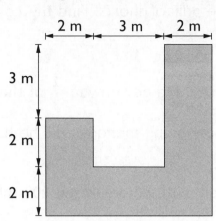

19. The figure is made up of a square and a semicircle. Find the shaded area in the figure. $\left(\text{Take } \pi = \dfrac{22}{7} \right)$

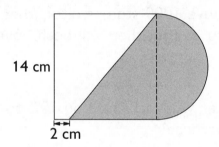

20. The shaded area is made up of an equilateral triangle and a quarter circle. Find its perimeter. (Take $\pi = 3.14$)

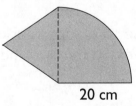

21. The figure is made up of 9 squares of the same size. If the perimeter of the figure is 128 cm, find the area of each square.

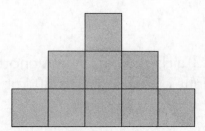

22. Extend the following tessellation in the space provided by drawing 5 more of the unit shape.

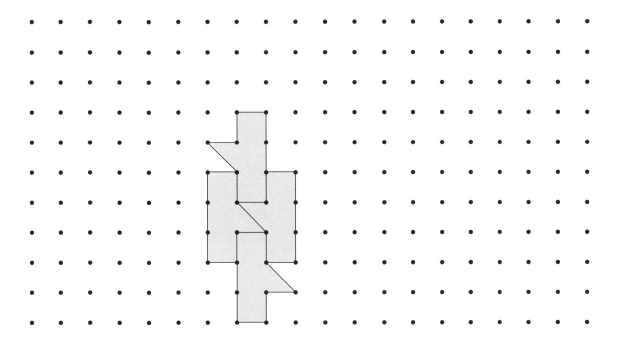

23. The bar graph shows what John does with his monthly salary.

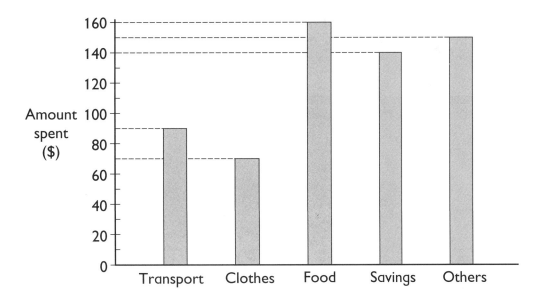

(a) How much more does John spend on food than on transport?

(b) What is John's monthly salary?

24. The total length of three ribbons, A, B and C is 2.6 m. Ribbon A is 60 cm longer than Ribbon B. Ribbon C is 50 cm longer than Ribbon B. Find the length of Ribbon A.

25. Gopal had some postcards for sale. He sold $\frac{3}{5}$ of them on Monday and the rest on Tuesday. If he sold 25 fewer postcards on Tuesday than on Monday, how many postcards did he have at first?

26. $\frac{1}{4}$ of the beads in a box are red. 60% of the remainder are yellow and the rest are blue. If there are 48 blue beads, how many beads are there altogether?

27. At 2:20 p.m., a van left Town A and traveled towards Town B at an average speed of 40 km/h. At 2:30 p.m., a car left Town B and traveled towards Town A along the same road at an average speed of 60 km/h. The car arrived at Town A at 3:30 p.m. What time did the van arrive at Town B?

28. Find the value of each of the following:

(a) $\frac{1}{4} + \frac{3}{4} \times 8 - \frac{1}{8}$

(b) $\frac{3}{5} \times (\frac{2}{3} \div \frac{1}{8}) + \frac{1}{2}$

EXERCISE 20

1. Each of the following solids is made up of 2-cm cubes. Find the volume of each solid.

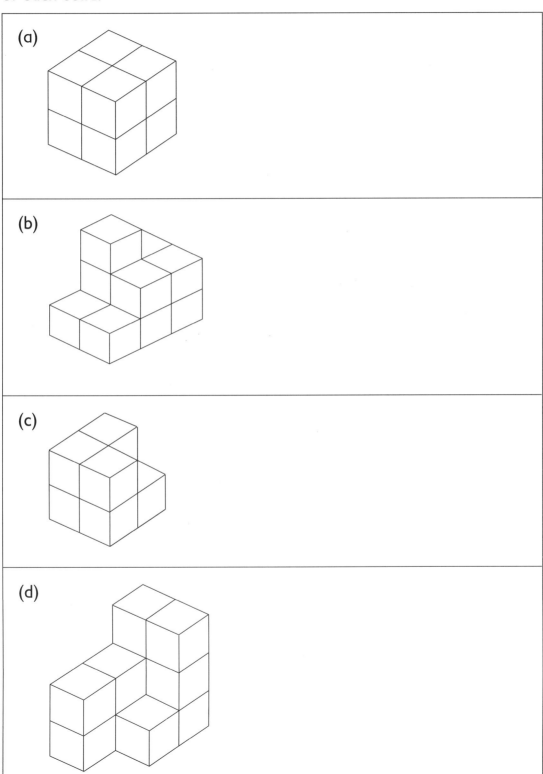

(a)

(b)

(c)

(d)

2. How many cubes of edge 2 cm are needed to build each of the following cuboids?

(a)

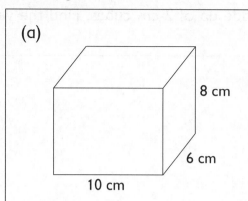

8 cm

6 cm

10 cm

(b)

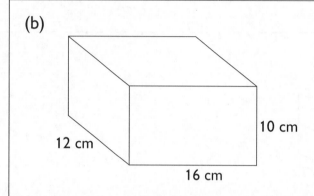

10 cm

12 cm

16 cm

3. Find the height of each cuboid.

(a)

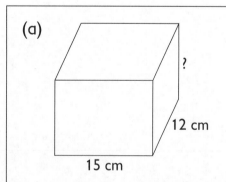

?

12 cm

15 cm

Volume = 1800 cm³

Height $= \dfrac{1800}{15 \times 12}$

$=$

(b)

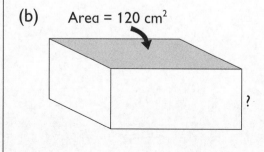

Area = 120 cm²

?

Volume = 720 cm³

EXERCISE 21

1. Find the volume of water in liters in each of the following rectangular containers. (1 liter = 1000 cm³)

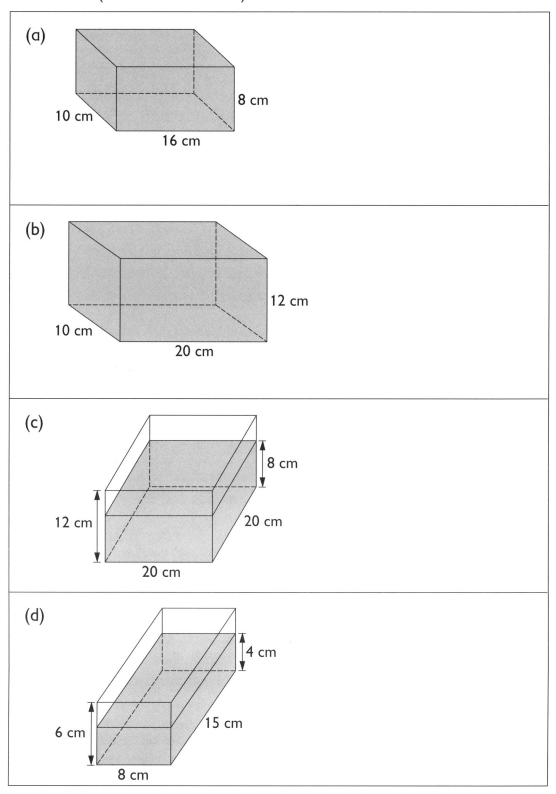

(a) 10 cm, 16 cm, 8 cm

(b) 10 cm, 20 cm, 12 cm

(c) 8 cm, 12 cm, 20 cm, 20 cm

(d) 4 cm, 6 cm, 15 cm, 8 cm

2. A rectangular container measuring 20 cm by 15 cm by 12 cm is $\frac{2}{3}$ filled with water. Find the volume of the water in liters. (1 liter = 1000 cm^3)

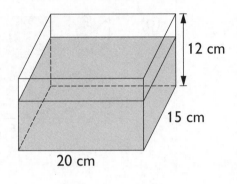

12 cm

15 cm

20 cm

3. A rectangular tank, 40 cm long and 30 cm wide, was filled with water to a depth of 20 cm. When Mary poured out some water from the tank, the water level dropped to 16 cm. How many liters of water did Mary pour out? (1 liter = 1000 cm^3)

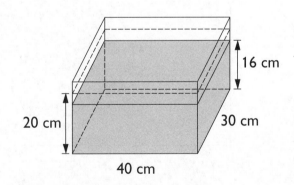

16 cm

20 cm

30 cm

40 cm

4. A rectangular tank is 60 cm long and 50 cm wide. It contains 42 liters of water when it is $\frac{1}{3}$ full. Find the height of the tank.
    (1 liter = 1000 cm³)

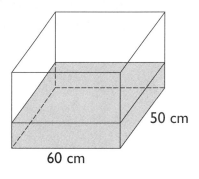

50 cm

60 cm

---

5. A rectangular tank, 60 cm long and 50 cm wide, is $\frac{4}{5}$ filled with water. When 24 liters of water are added, the water level rises to the brim of the tank. Find the height of the tank. (1 liter = 1000 cm³)

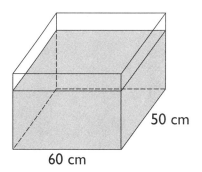

50 cm

60 cm

EXERCISE 22

1. A rectangular tank, 40 cm long and 30 cm wide, contained some water and a stone. The height of the water level was 15 cm. When the stone was taken out, the water level dropped to 9 cm. Find the volume of the stone.

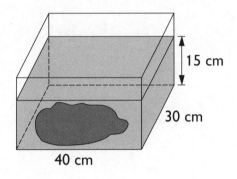

15 cm

30 cm

40 cm

2. A metal cube of edge 10 cm is placed in an empty rectangular tank measuring 30 cm by 25 cm by 15 cm. How many liters of water are needed to fill up the tank? (1 liter = 1000 cm³)

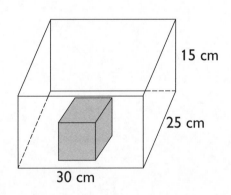

15 cm

25 cm

30 cm

3.   A rectangular tank, 50 cm long and 20 cm wide, contains water to a depth of 12 cm. When 4 identical metal balls are placed in the water, the water level rises to 16 cm. Find the volume of each ball.

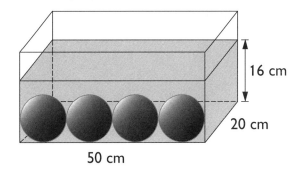

16 cm

20 cm

50 cm

4. A rectangular tank, 50 cm long and 30 cm wide, is $\frac{4}{5}$ filled with water. When 6 metal cubes of edge 10 cm are placed in the water, the water level rises to the brim of the tank. Find the height of the tank.

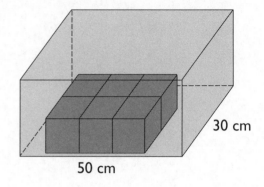

30 cm

50 cm

5. A rectangular tank measures 30 cm by 15 cm by 20 cm. It contains water to a depth of 15 cm. How many metal cubes of edge 5 cm need to be placed in the water to raise the water level to the brim of the tank?

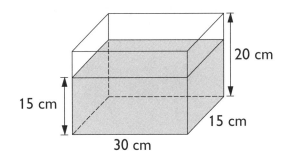

EXERCISE 23

1. An empty rectangular tank measures 40 cm by 30 cm by 15 cm. It is being filled with water flowing from a tap at a rate of 12 liters per minute. How long will it take to fill up the tank? (1 liter = 1000 cm³)

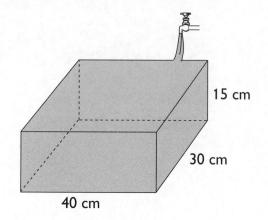

15 cm

30 cm

40 cm

2. A rectangular tank measuring 80 cm by 50 cm by 60 cm is filled with water to its brim. If the water is drained out at a rate of 15 liters per minute, how long will it take to empty the tank? (1 liter = 1000 cm³)

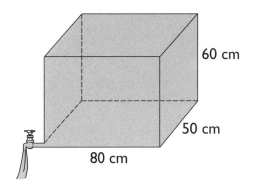

60 cm

50 cm

80 cm

3. A rectangular tank, 60 cm long and 40 cm wide, contains some water and 2 metal cubes of edge 10 cm. The height of the water level is 30 cm. If the water is drained out at a rate of 10 liters per minute, how long will it take to empty the tank? (1 liter = 1000 cm³)

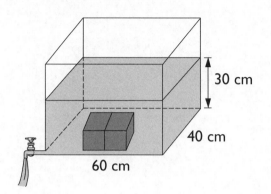

4. An empty rectangular tank, 40 cm long and 25 cm wide, contains 2 metal cubes of edge 10 cm. The tank is being filled with water flowing from a tap at a rate of 10 liters per minute. If it takes 3 minutes to fill up the tank, find the height of the tank. (1 liter = 1000 cm³)

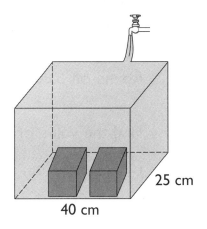

25 cm

40 cm

REVIEW 3

Write the answers in the boxes.

1. What is the missing number in the ■?

    $375.124 = 375 + ■ + 0.004$

2. Round off 5.806 to 2 decimal places.

3. Find the value of each of the following in its simplest form.

    (a) $2\frac{1}{4} - 1\frac{5}{8}$

    (b) $\frac{1}{5} \div \frac{2}{3} \times \frac{3}{4}$

4. Express $2\frac{3}{4}$ h in hours and minutes.

5. If $\frac{1}{4}$ of a number is 45, what is $\frac{1}{2}$ of the number?

6. 24 out of 40 children are boys. Find the ratio of the number of girls to the number of boys in its simplest form.

7. Express 0.045 as a percentage.

8. Find the value of 35% of 720 g.

9. Cameron took 1 hour and 15 minutes to travel from his house to his office. He left his house at 6:55 a.m. What time did he arrive at his office?

10. 3 chocolate bars cost $2.50. How many chocolate bars will cost $15?

11. The average height of 2 boys is 1.65 m. One boy is 0.02 m taller than the other. Find the height of the shorter boy.

12. Kevin spent $\frac{5}{8}$ of his money on a pair of shoes. He spent $\frac{1}{6}$ of the remaining money on a T-shirt. What fraction of his money did he have left?

13. $\frac{1}{3}$ of John's money is twice as much as Henry's money. If their total sum of money is $42, how much money does John have?

14. The ratio of the number of red beads to the number of black beads in a bag is 3 : 4. There are 39 red beads. How many more black beads than red beads are there?

15. The ratio of Dan's money to Tommy's money is 3 : 8. If Dan gives $\frac{1}{2}$ of his money to Tommy, what will be the new ratio of Dan's money to Tommy's money?

16. Colin's salary is increased by 10% to $1650. How much is the increase?

17. A machine caps 160 bottles every 2 minutes. At this rate, how long does it take to cap 400 bottles?

18. Mr. Bode takes 4 hours to complete a trip at an average speed of 60 km/h. If he increases his average speed to 80 km/h, how long will he take to complete the trip?

19. John bought x chairs at $45 each. In addition, he had to pay a delivery charge of $50. Express the total amount of money he paid in terms of x.

77

20. Four equal semicircular pieces were cut off from a rectangular piece of cardboard as shown. Find the area of the remaining cardboard. (Take π = 3.14)

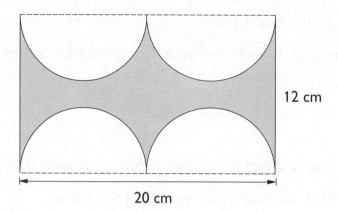

12 cm

20 cm

21. The figure is made up of a quarter circle and two semicircles. Find its perimeter in terms of π.

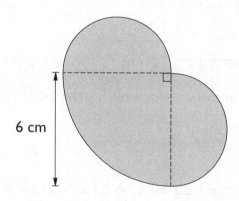

6 cm

22. A rectangular tank measures 90 cm by 50 cm by 60 cm. It contains 108 liters of water. Find the height of the water level in the tank. (1 liter = 1000 cm³)

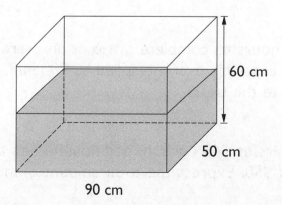

60 cm

50 cm

90 cm

23. The figure shows a solid that is made up of 10 unit cubes. Which of the following is the solid that remains when the two shaded cubes are removed?

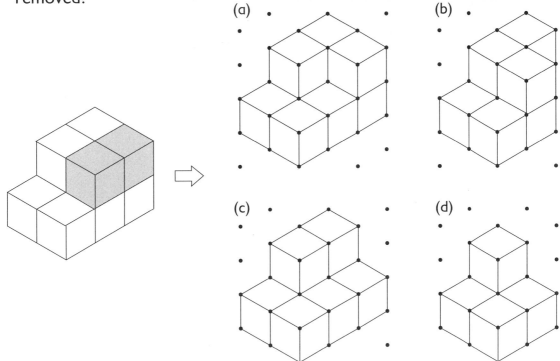

(a)

(b)

(c)

(d)

24. The line graph shows Suhua's savings over six months.

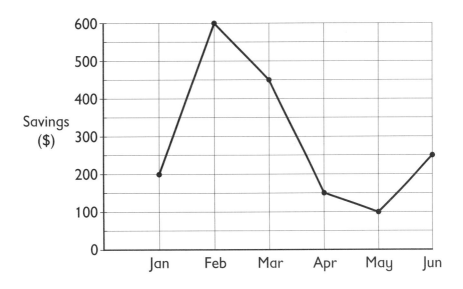

(a) How much did Suhua save in March?

(b) Find her average savings per month correct to the nearest dollar.

79

25. Jeff had 5 watches which were of the same cost price. He sold 3 of them at $110 each. He sold the rest at cost price. He received $490 altogether. How much money did he make?

---

26. Kelly spent $\frac{2}{5}$ of her money on a doll and $\frac{1}{2}$ of the remainder on a musical box. She spent $8 more on the doll than on the musical box. How much money did she have left?

REVIEW 4

Write the answers in the boxes.

1. Write $500 + 7 + \dfrac{9}{10} + \dfrac{4}{1000}$ as a decimal.

2. What is the missing number in each ■?

    (a) ■ $\times 5 + 5 + 5 + 5 = 7 \times 5$

    (b) $0.25 \div$ ■ $= 0.025$

3. Find the missing number in each ■.

    (a) $\dfrac{5}{8} = 5 :$ ■

    (b) $3 :$ ■ $: 4 = 12 : 28 : 16$

4. Which one of the following is the best estimate of the amount of water in the container?

    $0.7 \, \ell, \qquad 1.3 \, \ell, \qquad 1.7 \, \ell, \qquad 1.8 \, \ell$

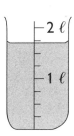

5. A car needs 4 liters of gas to travel 48 km. How many liters of gas does it need to travel 72 km?

6. If $\dfrac{1}{2}$ of a number is 15, what is 20% of the number?

7. The total cost of a shirt and 2 skirts is $46. The shirt costs twice as much as each skirt. Find the cost of the shirt.

8. The average weight of 3 boys is 41.5 kg. The average weight of 2 of them is 43.7 kg. Find the weight of the third boy.

9. Raju, Sita and Gopal shared a sum of money. Raju received $\frac{5}{8}$ of the money. Sita received $\frac{1}{3}$ of the remainder. Gopal received $40. How much was the sum of money shared by the three boys?

10. John's weight is $\frac{2}{3}$ of Peter's weight. Peter's weight is $\frac{6}{7}$ of Mary's weight. Find the ratio of Mary's weight to Peter's weight to John's weight.

11. Ahmad spent 40% of his money on a watch and 10% of the remainder on a radio. He spent $92 altogether. How much money did he have left?

12. The figure shows a quarter circle in a square. Find the area of the shaded part. (Take π = 3.14)

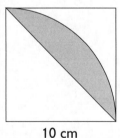

10 cm

13. The figure is made up of a square and two semicircles. Find its perimeter. $\left(\text{Take } \pi = \frac{22}{7} \right)$

7 cm

14. An empty box measures 10 cm by 6 cm by 6 cm. How many 2-cm cubes are needed to fill the box completely?

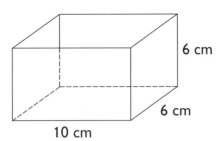

6 cm

6 cm

10 cm

15. The figure shows a solid consisting of 4 cubes of the same size. If the volume of the solid is 108 cm^3, find the area of the shaded face of the solid.

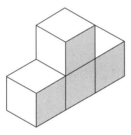

16. Which solid can be formed by the given net?

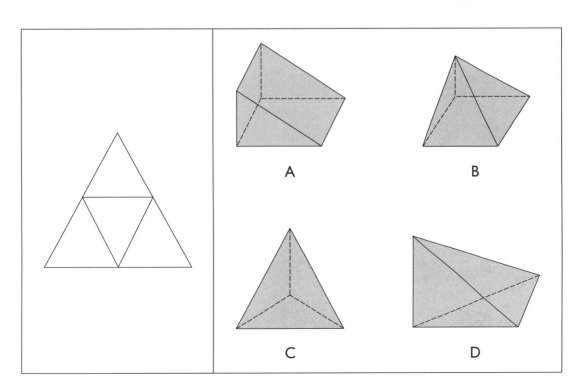

A

B

C

D

17. The pie chart shows how Mary spends her monthly salary.

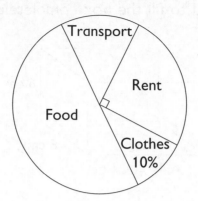

(a) What percentage of Mary's monthly salary is spent on rent?

(b) What percentage of her monthly salary is spent on transport?

(c) If she spends $200 on rent, how much does she spend on food?

18. At 8:00 a.m., Ryan left Town A and cycled towards Town B at 12 km/h. At the same time, Scott left Town B and cycled towards Town A at 16 km/h along the same road. At 8:30 a.m., they were still 4 km apart. Find the distance between the two towns.

EXERCISE 24

The following figures are not drawn to scale.

1. WXY is a right-angled triangle. XWV and XYZ are straight lines.
   Find $\angle y$.

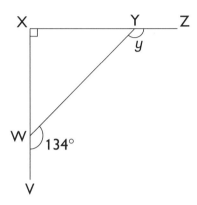

2. BCD is an isosceles triangle. ABC and EBD are straight lines. Find $\angle d$.

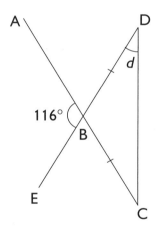

3. ABC and BDE are right-angled triangles. Find $\angle b$.

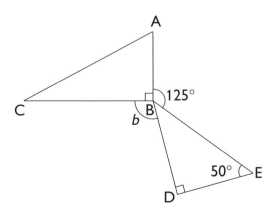

4. ABCD is a trapezoid.
   Find ∠x.

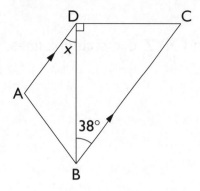

5. PQRS is a rhombus.
   Find ∠m.

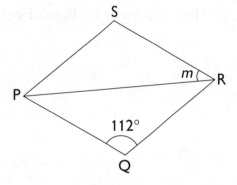

6. EFGH is a square.
   FHT is a straight line.
   Find ∠m.

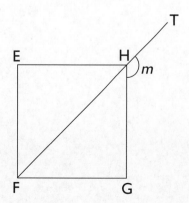

7. PQRS is a parallelogram.
   PQ ⊥ QT
   Find ∠x.

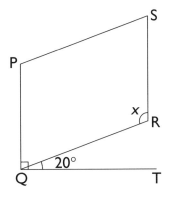

8. PQRS is a trapezoid.
   PQ ⊥ TQ
   Find ∠y.

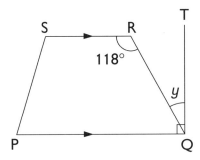

9. QRST is a parallelogram.
   PQR is a straight line.
   Find ∠x.

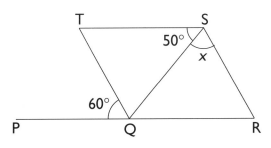

10. ABCD is a rhombus.
     CDE is a straight line.
     Find ∠a.

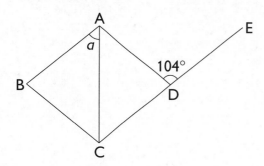

11. PQRS is a parallelogram.
     QRT is a straight line.
     Find ∠b.

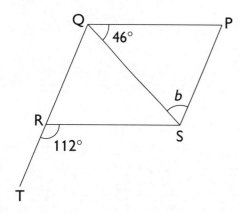

12. BCDE is a parallelogram.
     ABC is a straight line.
     Find ∠t.

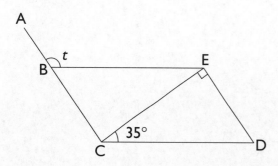

EXERCISE 25

The following figures are not drawn to scale.

1. ADC is a straight line.
    BD = AD
    Find $\angle d$.

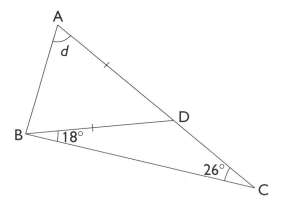

2. QRS is a straight line.
    PQ = PR = TR
    Find $\angle t$.

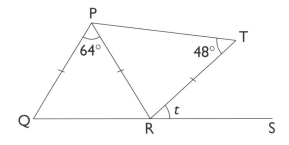

3. ABDE is a trapezoid.
    ABC is an equilateral triangle.
    Find $\angle r$.

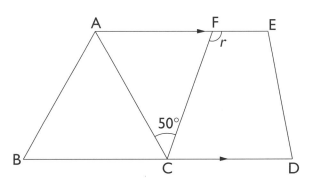

4. JKLM is a square.
MNP is a straight line.
MN = ML
Find ∠y.

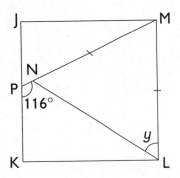

5. ABCD is a rectangle.
FCD is an equilateral triangle.
ECF is a straight line.
Find ∠p.

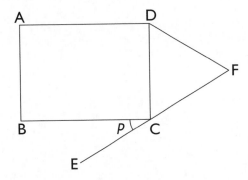

6. CDEF is a parallelogram.
DEG is a straight line.
EG = FG
Find ∠x.

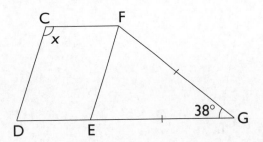

7. ABCD and ADEF are parallelograms.
Find ∠FAB.

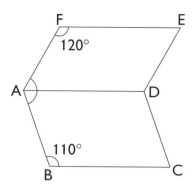

8. ABCD is a parallelogram.
AEF and BCF are straight lines.
AB = BF
Find ∠DAE.

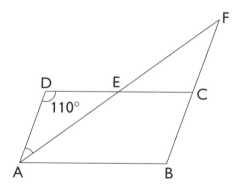

9. ABCD is a parallelogram.
ADE is a straight line.
AE ⊥ EC
Find ∠DAB.

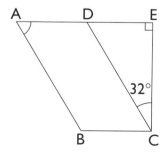

10. ABCD is a rhombus.
DBE is a straight line.
Find ∠EAB.

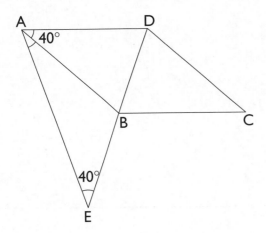

11. ABCD is a parallelogram.
AB = DB
Find ∠DCB.

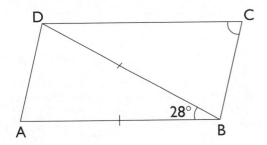

12. ABDE is a rectangle.
BCDF is a rhombus.
Find ∠AFB.

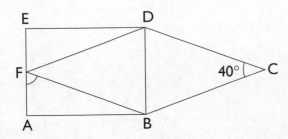

REVIEW 5

Write the answers in the boxes.

1. What is the missing number in each ■?

   (a) $574,296 = 504,296 + ■$

   (b) $\dfrac{5}{7} + \dfrac{3}{7} + \dfrac{2}{7} = ■ \times \dfrac{1}{7}$

2. Which one of the following is the best estimate of the value of 498×209?

   8000,   80,000,   10,000,   100,000

3. Express 0.34 as a percentage.

4. Find the value of 25% of $9.

5. In a test, Kelvin answered 15 out of a total of 20 questions correctly. What percentage of the questions did he answer correctly?

6. 6 pencils cost $2.40. Find the cost of 2 pencils.

7. A printing machine takes 6 minutes to print 300 pages. How many pages can it print in 15 minutes?

8. Andrew used a $50 bill to pay for 3 shirts. He received $18.50 change. Find the average cost of each shirt.

9. Rachel saved an average of $120 per month from January to March. She saved an average of $150 per month from January to April. How much did she save in April?

10. Dorothy bought 168 oranges. She threw away $\frac{1}{8}$ of them which were rotten. Then she gave $\frac{1}{3}$ of the remainder to her friends. How many oranges did she have left?

11. Nancy had $400. She spent $\frac{1}{4}$ of the money on a camera. She spent another $160 on a watch and saved the rest. What percentage of the money did she save?

12. The ratio of David's money to John's money is 3 : 5. They have $800 altogether. If David gives John $50, what will be the new ratio of David's money to John's money?

13. Jerome, Joe and Peter shared some stamps in the ratio 2 : 3 : 5. Peter received 60 more stamps than Jerome. Find the total number of stamps shared by the three boys.

14. A train is traveling at a speed of 120 km/h. How long will it take to travel a distance of 90 km?

15. Jordan took 3 hours to travel from Town X to Town Y. His average speed was 50 km/h. On his way back from Town Y to Town X, he took 1 hour less. Find his average speed for the return trip.

16. The length of the rectangle is 3 times its width. Express its perimeter in terms of a.

a cm

$3a$ cm

17. A quarter circle of radius 14 cm was cut off from a square as shown. Find the perimeter of the remaining figure. $\left(\text{Take } \pi = \dfrac{22}{7} \right)$

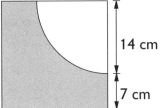

14 cm

7 cm

18. The figure shows a square and two semicircles. Find the area of the shaded part. (Take $\pi = 3.14$)

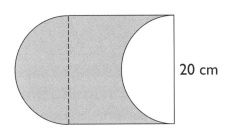

20 cm

19. A rectangular tank, measuring 60 cm by 35 cm by 36 cm, is filled with water to a depth of 14 cm. When a stone is placed in the water, the water level rises to $\dfrac{2}{3}$ of the height of the tank. Find the volume of the stone.

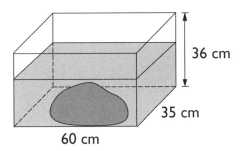

36 cm

35 cm

60 cm

20. In the figure, not drawn to scale, ACDE is a rectangle and ABCE is a parallelogram. Find $\angle$BAC.

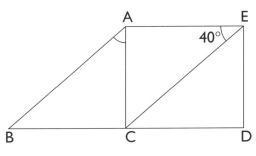

A   E
       40°
B   C   D

21. (a) In the space provided, draw a triangle ABC in which AB = 5 cm, AC = 6 cm and ∠BAC = 60°. (The line AB has been drawn for you.)

A   B

(b) Measure and write down the length of BC.

(Give your answer correct to 1 decimal place.)

22. The pie chart shows how Peter spent his money on his holiday.

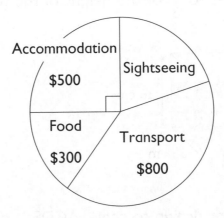

(a) How much did Peter spend altogether?

(b) How much did he spend on sightseeing?

(c) What fraction of the money was spent on transport?

23. A goldfish cost 3 times as much as a guppy. Gary spent $\frac{3}{5}$ of his money on 3 goldfish and 6 guppies and had $8 left. Find the cost of a goldfish.

24. The ratio of Samad's money to Hashim's money is 2 : 3. The ratio of Hashim's money to Rama's money is also 2 : 3. After Samad gives Hashim $\frac{1}{4}$ of his money, Rama has $30 more than Hashim. How much money did Samad have at first?

REVIEW 6

Write the answers in the boxes.

1. A number is a factor of 72. It is also a multiple of 8. What is the number if it is between 10 and 40?

2. How many $\frac{1}{2}$'s will make up $3\frac{1}{2}$?

3. A television program lasted $1\frac{3}{4}$ hours. It ended at 10:20 a.m. What time did it start?

4. Find the average of 6.8, 4.03 and 2.26 correct to 1 decimal place.

5. If 8 apples cost $3.60, find the cost of 12 apples.

6. 25% of a number is 13. What is $\frac{3}{4}$ of the number?

7. Thomas cycles 1 km in 4 minutes. What is his speed in m/min?

8. Martin spent $\frac{2}{3}$ of his money and gave $\frac{3}{4}$ of the remainder to his mother. He had $50 left. How much money did he have at first?

9. The membership of a club has increased from 25 to 35. By what percentage did the membership increase?

10. Kyle bought an oven for $240. He had to pay 3% sales tax. How much did he pay altogether?

11. There are 20% more men than women at a concert. If there are 420 men, how many more men than women are there?

12. The lengths of the 3 sides of a triangle are in the ratio 2 : 3 : 4. If the length of the shortest side is 4 in., find the perimeter of the triangle.

13. Henry, David and John shared $900 in the ratio 1 : 2 : 6. How much more money would Henry receive if the ratio was 2 : 3 : 5?

14. The ratio of Jake's money to Joe's money is 3 : 5. If Joe gives Jake $25, they will each have an equal amount of money. How much money do they have altogether?

15. Mr. Miles drove a distance of 150 km from Town A to Town B. His average speed for the trip was 60 km/h. How much time would he save if he increased his average speed for the trip by 15 km/h?

16. The figure is made up of a square and a semicircular shape. Find the perimeter of the figure. $\left(\text{Take } \pi = \dfrac{22}{7} \right)$

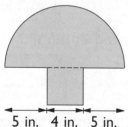

5 in. 4 in. 5 in.

17. The figure shows two circles of radii 3 m and 1 m respectively. Find the area of the shaded part in terms of π.

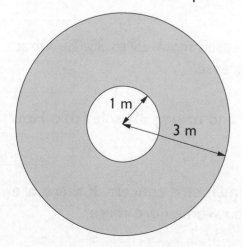

1 m

3 m

18. The figure is made up of a square and two triangles. Find its area.

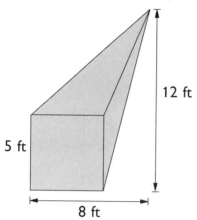

12 ft

5 ft

8 ft

19. A rectangular tank, measuring 64 cm by 50 cm by 40 cm, is $\frac{3}{4}$ filled with water. If the water is drained out at a rate of 12 liters per minute, how long will it take to empty the tank? (1 liter = 1000 cm³)

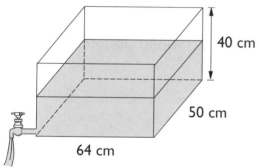

40 cm

50 cm

64 cm

20. In the figure, not drawn to scale, PQRS is a parallelogram and TR = SR. Find ∠PQR.

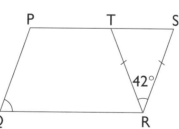

P   T   S

42°

Q   R

21. In the figure, not drawn to scale, ABCD is a rhombus and BED is an equilateral triangle. Find ∠BAD.

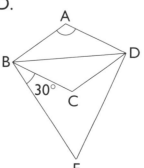

A

B   D

30°
C

E

22. Find the ratio of the volume of Solid A to the volume of Solid B.

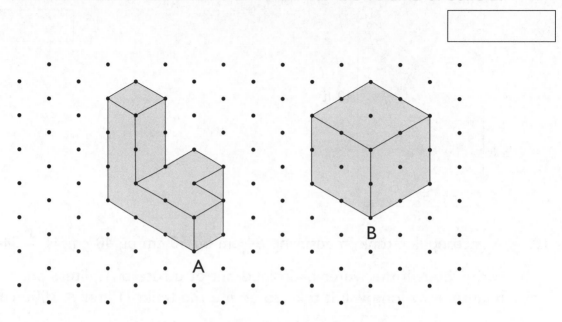

23. The pie chart represents the amounts of money donated by four 6th grade classes.

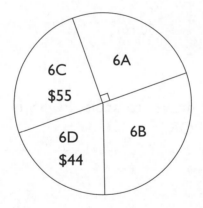

(a) What percentage of the total amount of money was donated by 6C?

(b) What was the total amount of money donated by the four classes?

(c) How much money was donated by 6B?

(d) Find the ratio of the amount of money donated by 6C to the amount of money donated by 6D.

24. Ali had $120. He had $45 more than his brother. After his brother spent some money on a toy, Ali had twice as much money as his brother. Find the cost of the toy.

25. There were 20% more boys than girls in a swimming club. After 50 girls left, there were twice as many boys as girls in the club. How many boys were there in the club?

REVIEW 7

Write the answers in the boxes.

1. Write $\dfrac{3}{100} + 4 + \dfrac{5}{10}$ as a decimal.

2. Find the value of $28 + 15 \div 5 \times 3$.

3. $\dfrac{3}{8}$ of a number is 27. What is $\dfrac{1}{2}$ of the number?

4. Find the value of 1.53×260.

5. Find the value of $\dfrac{5}{9} \div \dfrac{2}{3}$.

6. Express 3 kg 50 g in kilograms.

7. 3 girls and 2 boys shared $140. Each boy received twice as much money as each girl. How much money did each boy receive?

8. Morgan has 240 stickers. The number of Anne's stickers is $\dfrac{3}{4}$ of the number of Morgan's stickers. How many stickers do they have altogether?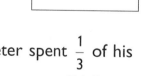

9. Peter had 3 times as much money as Larry. After Peter spent $\dfrac{1}{3}$ of his money, he still had $50 more than Larry. How much money did Peter have at first?

10. John bought a bag of balloons. $\dfrac{1}{5}$ of the balloons were red, $\dfrac{3}{8}$ of the remainder were yellow and the rest were blue. If there were 25 blue balloons, how many red balloons were there?

105

11. John, Peter and David shared a sum of money in the ratio 4 : 3 : 2. What fraction of the sum of money did John receive?

[ ]

12. The ratio of the number of red beads to the number of blue beads is 2 : 3. The ratio of the number of red beads to the number of yellow beads is 4 : 3. What is the ratio of the number of red beads to the total number of blue beads and yellow beads?

[ ]

13. There are 400 people at a concert. 55% of them are men, 25% are women and the rest are children. How many more adults than children are there?

[ ]

14. Andrew, Sean and Connor shared some stamps. Andrew received 25% of the stamps. The ratio of the number of Sean's stamps to Connor's was 2 : 3. If Connor received 60 more stamps than Sean, how many stamps did Andrew receive?

[ ]

15. Mr. Rand took 20 minutes to travel from Town A to Town B. His average speed was 66 km/h. Find the distance between the two towns.

[ ]

16. Josh cycled from Town A to Town B. He took $\frac{3}{4}$ hour to cycle $\frac{1}{4}$ of the trip at 16 km/h. He cycled the remaining trip at 12 km/h. He reached Town B at 10:30 a.m. What time did he leave Town A?

[ ]

17. If $a = 4$, find the value of $3 - \frac{a}{3}$.

[ ]

18. A glass costs $x and a jug costs $9. Find the total cost of 6 glasses and 2 jugs in terms of x.

[ ]

19. A piece of wire is bent to form the figure which is made up of two semicircles as shown. Find the length of the wire. $\left(\text{Take } \pi = \dfrac{22}{7}\right)$

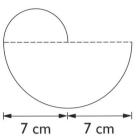

7 cm   7 cm

20. A rectangular tank, 30 cm long and 20 cm wide, is filled with water to a depth of 8 cm. When a stone is placed in the water, the water level rises to $\dfrac{2}{3}$ of the height of the tank. If the volume of the stone is 2400 cm³, find the height of the tank.

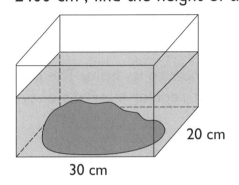

20 cm

30 cm

21. In the figure, not drawn to scale, ABCD is a parallelogram, AD = AE and CAE is a straight line. Find ∠ADE.

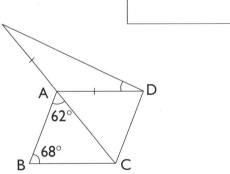

22. In the figure, not drawn to scale, PQRT is a square and RST is an equilateral triangle. Find ∠SQR.

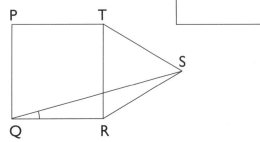

23. Use the given shape to make a tessellation in the space provided.

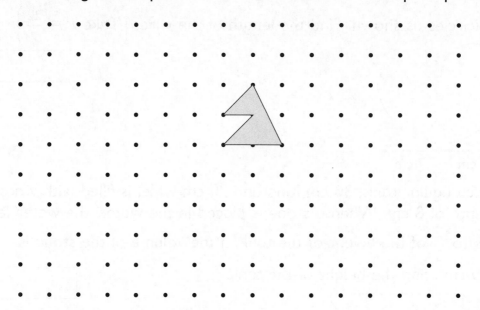

24. A tap was turned on to fill a tank with water to its brim. The line graph shows the volume of water in the tank at regular intervals of time.

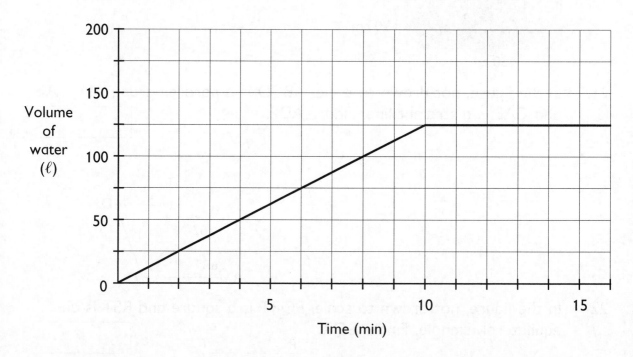

(a) What was the volume of water in the tank when it was full?

(b) How long did it take to fill the tank to its brim?

25. The ratio of the number of girls to the number of boys in a stamp club was 3 : 2 last year. When 15 boys joined the club this year, the ratio became 2 : 3. Find the total number of children in the club this year.

26. Jesse drove from Town A to Town B. At 8:30 a.m., he had traveled $\frac{2}{3}$ of the trip. He traveled the remaining trip at an average speed of 80 km/h and reached Town B at 8:45 a.m. If his average speed for the whole trip was 90 km/h, what time did he leave Town A?

27. Mrs. Garcia divided $\frac{2}{5}$ of a cake equally among her 4 children. How much cake did each child get?

Give the answer in its simplest form.

---

28. Which one of the following has the smallest value?

(a) $\frac{1}{6}$

(b) 0.116

(c) 0.16

29. What is the ratio of 6 c to 3 gal 2 c?
    Give the answer in its simplest form.

---

30. How many 1 pt bottles can be filled with 6.5 gal of water?